Contents

Written by Lisa Regan
Illustrated by Angelika Scudamore

First published 2018 by Brown Watson
The Old Mill, 76 Fleckney Road
Kibworth Beauchamp
Leicestershire LE8 0HG

ISBN: 978 0 7097 2597 8
© 2018 Brown Watson, England
Reprinted 2018
Printed in Malaysia

Now I Can READ

Magical Tales

Brown Watson

ENGLAND

The Secret Stone

Princess Eleanor was feeling very lucky. She had lots and lots of presents to open for her birthday. She couldn't wait to wear her new dresses!

She had just one present that was most strange. It was from someone called Prince Antonio. She didn't know who he was. It was a very peculiar, quite ugly piece of stone. It wasn't pretty at all.

She put it by her bed and
went out to play. That night,
as she slept, the stone began
to glow. It grew brighter and
brighter until it woke
Princess Eleanor up.

As she gazed at the stone, she
could see inside it. There was
a unicorn! Princess Eleanor
reached out, and as her hand
touched the smooth surface, she
felt herself being whisked away.

Princess Eleanor found herself on the unicorn's back, flying through the air. They swooped and swirled and chased shooting stars.

As the night sky faded into morning, the unicorn flew into Eleanor's bedroom. The princess climbed back under the covers. 'That is the best birthday present EVER!' she gasped. She couldn't wait for her next adventure!

Read these words again

away	wait
under	flying
next	stone
back	began
felt	night
play	found
ugly	herself

What can you see here

dress

lamp

present

star

drawers

shoe

Fairy Lights

Princess Carolina loves to sing. She sings everywhere. She sings at breakfast, and the birds come to sit on the table and listen.

She sings in the bath, and the squirrels hop onto the windowsill to hear her songs. It makes Princess Carolina smile.

One day, Princess Carolina noticed something strange. Whenever she sang, little lights twinkled in the forest. When she went quiet, the lights disappeared.

Princess Carolina walked to the edge of the forest and began to sing quietly. Sure enough, the lights were there. They grew brighter as she sang more loudly.

Suddenly, Carolina saw one of the lights fly past. Oh! It was a little fairy, glowing in the darkness of the forest. She waved her tiny hand for Carolina to follow her.

The fairy led Carolina into a hollow tree trunk. Carolina gasped. It was full of fairy folk! They asked her to sing again, and the whole tree lit up. Her songs provided magical power for fairyland!

Read these words again

past	birds
songs	bath
hand	again
onto	power
little	quiet
tree	strange
loves	waved

What can you see here?

fairy house

bird

lights

cup

kettle

leaf

The Show Must Go On

The sun is shining. It is a beautiful day in fairyland. 'Would you like some more fairyberry juice?' asks Sparkle. 'Hot days make me thirsty!'

The fairies finish their picnic and pack away their dirty plates and glasses. They need the space to practise for their fairy show.

Sparkle, Glitter, Twinkle and Sunbeam work out their new dance steps. They will be the first to go on stage and they want it to be perfect.

Then it begins to rain. Small drops turn into bigger drops, and soon it is raining so hard that their wings don't work. They shelter under a big tree and hope the rain stops soon.

Twinkle won't let a rain shower spoil their show. She waves her wand and a beautiful canopy of blossom covers their stage.

The fairies carry on practising until the rain stops. They have had plenty of time to perfect their steps to show to everyone. 'Brilliant! Hooray!' cheer the audience. 'Do another dance!'

Read these words again

pack

steps

time

tree

rain

space

show

stops

cheer

perfect

hard

wings

another

more

What can you see here?

cake

jug

daisy

fairy

curtains

bird

Magical Maisie

Maisie is in her bedroom. Her spell book lies open on her bed. Which spell should she try today? Aha! That looks like a good one. She points her wand and says the magic words.

BAM! Maisie turns her cushion into a giant trampoline. She has great fun bouncing up and down until her legs are tired.

Maisie checks her spell book and turns the trampoline back into a cushion. Then she finds a different page. BAM! Her toy cars become real life racing cars. Maisie spends ages zooming around the track.

She finds the spell to turn the cars back into toys. Then she says more magic words and points her wand at her favourite teddy. BAM!

Ooh! Perhaps this was a bad idea. Now her teddy is a big, scary bear! Maisie hides under her bed, but now she can't reach her spell book. She closes her eyes and thinks very hard.

BAM! Maisie casts a spell to bring her book under the bed next to her. Now she can see what she must do to turn the bear back into a fluffy teddy once again.

Read these words again

bedroom   hides

spell   eyes

magic   casts

trampoline   fluffy

bouncing   teddy

zooming   points

favourite   thinks

What can you see here?

wand

bed

wheel

clock

flag

cushion

Lazy Days

Jess lay on her back and watched the clouds drift across the sky. Her daddy finished eating and lay on the rug next to her. 'I see a cow!' he said. 'And a bike!'

'I see a toadstool!' laughed Jess. 'And a fairy.'

Soon, she could hear daddy snoring in the sunshine.

Penny gave a bark and ran off into the bushes. Jess thought she should follow her to check she was okay. As she crawled under the branches, she heard tinkling bells and chattering voices.

Jess stopped and peeped out. Oh! She could see lots of tiny creatures, dancing and laughing in front of her. She stayed out of sight and watched.

The fairies were having great
fun, until Penny ran right
through the middle of their
party. The music stopped and
they scattered in all directions.

Jess hurried back to her
daddy and lay down on the rug.
Should she tell him what she
had seen? Then a tiny fairy flew
close by. She gave Jess a wink
and put her finger to her lips.
It was a secret!

Read these words again

clouds

drift

cow

rug

toadstool

snoring

bark

crawled

branches

chattering

peeped

scattered

wink

secret

What can you see here?

dog

bee

fairy

beetle

sandwich

apple

Hatty's Hats

Hatty was getting ready to play. She brushed her teeth, put on her clothes, and looked in the mirror. Hmm, which hat should she wear today?

It was very important to choose the right hat. Each one was special. Exciting things happened when she wore them! She chose her penguin hat and got ready for an adventure.

Hatty shivered and pulled her hat over her ears. It was very, very cold. She could see snow and ice all around her. Was she at the South Pole?

Hatty laughed as lots of penguins zoomed past. They were sliding on their tummies on the ice. Hatty sat down and lifted up her feet. She pushed with her hands and soon she was sliding too!

'Hello!' shouted Hatty as she slid past a baby penguin. The little chick gave a nervous squeak and flapped its wings. What could be wrong?

Hatty looked ahead to see the penguins diving off the edge of the ice. Help! She reached up and pulled off her hat. Phew, just in time! Instead of landing in the ocean, she bounced back onto her bed in her cosy room. That was close!

Read these words again

brushed	sliding
teeth	tummies
special	pushed
penguin	squeak
adventure	flapped
shivered	ocean
ice	cosy

What can you see here?

ball

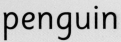

penguin

hat

teddy

book

boots

53

Where Are You?

Twinkle is playing her favourite game. She has to cover her eyes while all of her friends run and hide. Then she has to try to find them.

Twinkle counts to twenty while they hide. Sanjay Squirrel covers himself with leaves and Holly Hedgehog scuttles behind a bush. Twinkle finds them both easily!

Twinkle has to look harder for Rosie Rabbit and Candy Crow. That just leaves Franny Frog to find. She is nowhere to be seen.

The game lasts for so long that Twinkle asks her friends to help her. Eventually, they find Franny on the pond. She was pretending to be a statue!

They all begin to giggle as they realise how clever Franny is. She gets the prize for winning the game. It is a medal made of a daisy.

Twinkle giggles. 'And you have given me an idea for a new game,' she says. 'Who wants to play musical statues?'

Read these words again

game   behind

lasts   find

eyes   twenty

long   just

prize   easily

seen   help

pond   cover

What can you see here?

frog

flower

toadstool

fish

rabbit

hedgehog

Over the Rainbow

Abby opened the stable doors wide. 'Come out to play, Petal!' she called to her magical pet unicorn. 'It is a beautiful day!'

Petal and Abby galloped off. Soon, the blue sky turned grey and rain began to fall. It fell so hard that it hurt Abby's head. Petal's tail turned soggy and her mane hung in her eyes.

Abby had an idea. She whispered in Petal's ear. Petal shook the water from her mane and tail. She began to run as fast as she could, along the path and out of the trees.

Petal ran faster and Abby held on very tight. Then Petal's hooves lifted off the ground, and they were flying! Soon, they were high in the sky, above the clouds and the rain.

They flew through the air and danced in the sunbeams. When Petal was tired, they slid down a rainbow and landed gently on the ground.

Abby took off Petal's reins. She brushed her mane and coat until they were silky smooth again. 'Thank you for being my friend,' whispered Abby. 'We will always look after each other, won't we?'

Read these words again

stable

beautiful

galloped

grey

soggy

mane

idea

whispered

fast

tight

flying

sunbeams

slid

silky

What can you see here?

tiara

bird

heart

rainbow

rabbit

squirrel

Accidents will Happen

Ella is in a hurry. Mummy has made her lunch and she is very, very hungry. Ella rushes from her room as fast as she can. OOOOOPS!

Poor Ella trips over her cat and falls to the floor. ZAP! Oh, Ella. Accidents like this always happen to her.

Ella is learning how to make potions. She is trying really, really hard to get it right this time. No more accidents! She carefully adds the last spoonful of sugar.

The potion bubbles up with a loud BANG! Ella jumps high in the air and splashes potion onto her shoes. It makes them spark and fizz. OOOOOPS!

The potion is finished and
nothing else has gone wrong.
Ella can't wait to tell her
mummy. She pours some into
a bottle and puts on the lid.
Slowly does it! Then she shouts
for Mummy to come and look.

Mummy bursts through the door
and knocks over the potion.
Oh, Mummy! Now they can't
see a thing!

Read these words again

lunch

hungry

rushes

trips

potions

carefully

sugar

bubbles

spark

jumps

pours

shouts

bursts

knocks

What can you see here?

 vase

 cauldron

 hat

 bottle

 cat

 picture

77

The Good Fairies

Not all fairies are full of light and happiness. Some of them are grumpy and mean, and live in the dark. It makes them play naughty tricks on the humans that live nearby.

Tricksy, Mallory and Vanessa are bad fairies. They live in a gloomy cave under a giant oak tree, where they plot and plan their next piece of naughtiness.

The good fairies want to help the bad fairies. They think they could be generous and kind, and do good deeds for the humans.

Layla and Sunbeam have an idea. They find their favourite fairy lights to give to the bad fairies. 'If they don't live in a dark and gloomy place, they might be nicer!'

Sure enough, Tricksy and her
friends feel much happier.
They even sneak into a child's
bedroom at night to give her
sweet dreams.

The good fairies are very happy.
'We have more lights for you,
and a reward for your good
deeds. Close your eyes while we
bring it in. SURPRISE!'

Read these words again

give   might
eyes   idea
very   bring
dark   humans
sweet   place
plan   think
cave   kind

What can you see here?

glass

daisy

toadstool

cake

bowl

butterfly

85

To the Rescue

'Oh no! Oh no!' shouted the boy as he ran into the royal hall. 'The dragon is on the loose again! It has already frightened off all of our sheep!'

'What can we do to make it go away?' asked the King. Abby jumped up from the table. 'I can help!' she shouted.

Abby and her pet unicorn
Petal raced off to the forest
to find out where the dragon was
hiding. Abby put an arrow into
her bow and pointed it
at the dragon.

'You can choose what happens,'
she said. 'Either you stop
scaring our animals, and come
to the palace for tea every day...
or I will chase you far, far away.
Which will it be?'

The dragon agreed to stop scaring the animals. 'But only if I can have cake?' he asked.

Abby galloped home to tell her parents about her deal. The King was very happy, and the Queen was very relieved. They had a huge party to celebrate – with a piece of cake for everyone!

Read these words again

royal

loose

frightened

sheep

raced

forest

choose

pointed

scaring

palace

chase

tea

galloped

celebrate

What can you see here?

queen

 firework

arrow

dragon

king